The ups & downs of being in your FIFTIES

The ups & downs of being in your FIFTIES

Tony Husband

ARCTURUS

ARCTURUS

This edition published in 2019 by Arcturus Publishing Limited
26/27 Bickels Yard, 151–153 Bermondsey Street,
London SE1 3HA

ISBN: 978-1-78828-363-2
AD006043UK

Printed in China

INTRODUCTION

Not long ago, being in your 50s was considered ancient. As a result, people got up to strange things, like wearing their slippers to the shops, talking about other people's operations with morbid relish, and driving at 50mph in the middle lane of the motorway.

But times have changed and now no one thinks of people in their 50s as old. Why, they're barely middle-aged! And if your children haven't left home yet and your elderly parents also need looking after, then you belong to the Sandwich Generation and you no longer have time to be old.

When I hit 50, I came to think of grey hair as rather an attractive feature, a bit like forgetting everyone's name – that's what I told myself anyway. With age comes knowledge, or the confidence to think you have knowledge. I became outspoken on many things, the environment, politics, religion, Manchester United, though the last two are the same thing.

These days Nifty Fifties can have it all. They go to the gym at least once a week, eat a power-packed diet and chat openly to their kids about what's going on (in theory anyway). This keeps them fit for all the challenges they face. With experience to match their energy, they're in peak condition to be the best taxi driver, chef, confidant and cashier at the Bank of Mum and Dad their family could ever hope for.

Tony Husband

'Hi, Joan, it's Trish. You've been 50 for quite a while now.
Have you got any tips?'

'Mm, is it me or is this path suddenly getting steeper?'

'Now the children have left home, it's just you and me and the wine, Keith. That's scary.'

Male 53 looking for companionship. Willing to travel.

'Aagh! I've got fewer FB friends than I had in my 40s!!'

'Just had the most terrible nightmare, Rod. I dreamt I was in my 60s... and you did nothing to help!'

'I'm worried about Mary. She's just bought me a Brad Pitt mask.'

'Looking 50 is great, but only if you happen to be 60 or 70.'

'You're a dark horse, Brian. I never would have thought that dating Angelina Jolie would be number 4 on your bucket list.'

'I'm 51. Am I too young to complain about the neighbours'
wheelie-bins?'

'From up here, Jan, I can see Wilkinson's bald patch is bigger than mine... and he's not even 50 yet.'

'For crying out loud, Ned, just admit you need glasses.'

'All's well with the world, Edith. I've just remembered my PIN number.'

'Hmmm, not bad for my mid–50s! Give me a quick nip and tuck and some low lighting and I'll be irresistible again.'

'Well, I hope I look as good as you do when I'm in my 60s.'
'Actually, I'm in my 50s.'

'This is our fourth wine-tasting this week.'

'I'm 57. Anyone got a problem with that?'

'Tell me honestly, Toby. Do I look 56?'

'First, it was all that para-gliding, then there was the big motorbike and, after that, his affair. I don't know how many more of his mid-life crises I can take.'

'Not the most successful of classes, were we?'

'To be honest, Stan, I'm glad you're retiring soon.'

28

'Great master, how do you survive your 50s?' 'It always helps if you keep your fingers crossed.'

'Tinnitus? How on earth did I get that?'

'It's never too late to learn Mandarin. That's why I've put you down for the course.'

'Go on, marks out of ten... How cool do I look?'

'She said now the children have left home, she wants to get a monkey.'

'I admire you looking for new challenges at your age, Bob, but I'm not sure about escapology. You've been in there for hours.'

'I thought you'd be happy you're going to be a grandma, darling.'

'Go on, how old do you think I am?' 'Er, 44.'

'I woke up feeling too cheerful, so I'm sticking this on.'

'Stop worrying, he said he'd bring his best friend.'

'What girl in the cake?'

'Looks like Hobson's got the push.'

'Apparently, 80 per cent of men in their 50s still think they look like they did in their 40s.'

'Quiet in here tonight.'

'Come on. Remember, Alan, no pain, no gain.'

'If I was your wife, I'd give you poison.'
'If you were my wife, I'd take it.'

'There he goes! Does my bum look big in that?'

'Jo, wake up. Look, I've got 1,000 Twitter followers.'

'The speakers? Ah yes, I have a lot of garden parties.'

'You know the tree house you built for the kids all those years ago?
Why don't you move into it for a while now they've gone?'

'Stop staring at me like that... I'm trying!!'

'I'm missing hen parties.'

'Funny, when I was in my 40s mole hills didn't bother me one bit, but now they make me mad. Grrrr!'

'Darling, lots of people are 58.'

'If we won the lottery, we could go to Bridlington for a long weekend.'

'Yes, Felicity, he does look good for his age, but remember all that glistens is not gold.'

'It's not that I don't fancy you any more... it's just that you're, er, in your 50s.'

'Grumpy old man?! I'm only 55!!'

'Since James turned 50, he's become a reckless fool.'

'Very impressive, Nigel, but perhaps your legs need a bit more work.'

'I think I'm 50 today.'

'Martha, look, 60 is coming!'
'Lie down, Phil. It's just a terrible nightmare.'

'We've been coming here for 20 years, Jack, and you're still trying
to impress me by eating Vindaloo.'

'Mendelssohn, Beethoven, Bach... I'll hide the lightweight stuff until the Smythes have gone home.'

'I'm sorry about Bob. At home, he has a spittoon by his chair.'

'54 years old and he still goes to bed with his teddy.'

'Have you seen my flip-flops anywhere?'

'We've got this massive house. Trouble is, the mortgage is so big we can't afford to go out.'

'Ignoring it won't make it go away.'

'You were doing 54. What a coincidence: same as your age!'

'Great, Syd. I'm sure there aren't many old codgers who can break dance like that.'

'Do you remember when we used to hold hands walking down the street?'

'My dad said I'd be a millionaire by the time I reached 50. Boy, did he get that wrong.'

'Look at us, Brian. We're in our 50s and we're still the best-looking couple in the room...'

'In his 40s, we used to go for a jog twice a day. Now he just sits there.'

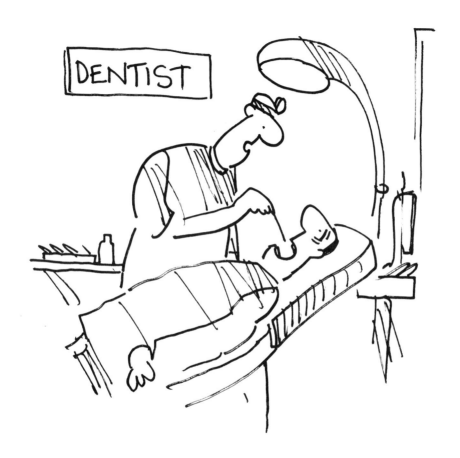

'Hold this tongue-depresser down for me while I fetch the big drill.'

'I'm guessing you're in your 50s, sir. There are two ways you can go:
Ferrari, or perhaps something a little more sensible.'

'Happy 50th, Jen. Hop on the back and don't forget to pedal.'

'To be honest, at my age I don't want to be straying off the beaten track every time we go away.'

'I could have been bigger than Beckham if it hadn't been for the beer.'

'It's uncanny: the older I get, the younger I feel.'

'Lovely boiled egg, darling, but please explain why I can't have soldiers any more now I'm 50?'

'Look, Dad's 87. If he rings and asks me to go for a pint, I can't turn him down.'

'Ah, I see you found my vitamin cupboard.'

'If I keep watching the clock, it'll seem much longer until I'm 60.'

'It's the care home. Your father's done his back in break dancing.'

'Excuse me, old lady, would you like a seat?'

'Aarggh (gasp)... Remind me to google "sports for the over-50s" when we get back.'

'Tom, the important thing was to finish the marathon. Why worry if 1,486 people in their 60s came in ahead of you?'

'That's nearly our combined age! Who'd want to live to 100?'
'Someone who's 99?!'

'For my 51st, can I have an electric train set?'

'OK, class, any questions?' 'What's it like being very old, Miss?'

'I'm drinking too much, doc. Want a snifter?'

'Get in there... I've been accepted for Big Brother.'

'Best head home... my wife's asking where I am in capital letters.'

'Hi, come in, darling. Do try some of my "Make Your 50s Fun" cocktail. (hic)'

'The problem I find with my driving now I'm in my 50s is that I'm too near the ball once I've hit it.'

'You're obsessed with getting a tan, aren't you, Bob?'

'That racket was our daughter trying to squeeze through the cat–flap
after she left her keys in the pub.'

'Pete, I need a new dishwasher. I'm divorcing you.'

'We've spent so long talking about the good old days and now they're really here.'

'Hi, mate, get down to the pub quick. I think our luck's in. I'm chatting up two desperate 50-year-olds.'

'This satnav is telling me you've visited "Bert's Betting Shop" 27 times in the last three weeks.'

'Ever felt past your sell-by date, Nancy?'

'Tess, can you serve those two old dears over there?'

'Yes, darlings, we still go to Glastonbury every year. We recapture the free spirit of our youth by glamping in a luxury yurt.'

'Look at Mr Smug over there — retired and on a huge pension at 51.'

'Six months ago, he morphed into a very annoying 50-something with exceedingly dull opinions.'

'Goodness, looks like they'll be showing off their holiday tans.'

'Hi, yeah I'm here on a train, sat next to a bunch of really boring business blokes in their 50s.'

'Right, kids, time to draw straws. The one who draws the shortest has to move out and find their own place.'

'Your son's in the Middle East doing humanitarian work. You must be very proud.' 'No, we're terrified.'

'Monica, this is Allan. He's a crashing bore too.'

'I'm in my 50s. Can I delete my medical records and start again?'

'That was Alice. She's having a Prosecco and Tupperware party!'

'Good for you, mister... in your 50s and still out and about.'

'Hic... sssh; keep the noise down.
My wife will never suspect a thing (hic).'

'Ha, I wanted to be a jockey ... You wanted to be a ballerina.'

'Darling, we've played it safe for too long!'

'As if buying me a wheelbarrow for my 50th is going to sort out her
flipping garden for her...'

'His IT results are well below average — all too often the case for children with "older" parents.'

'What a truly delightful walk. Some chap said she's beautiful like her mum. I said I'm not her mum; I'm her gran. Never, he said.'

'Blooming heck, Paul, you're just as boring as you were back then.'

'Part of me says you're in your 50s, be sensible;
another part says go for it, girl.'

'Now that the last one has left, we're going to have so much more time to ourselves.'

'Those flippin' noisy 50-somethings in the flat upstairs!'